I Love Cats

BY PAM BROWN

EDITED BY MARTIN KERR

Helen Exley®

Published in 2015 by Helen Exley® Gift books in Great Britain.
Edited by Martin Kerr
Design, selection and editing © Helen Exley Creative Ltd 2015
Words by Pam Brown © Helen Exley Creative Ltd 2015.
Photography © Yoneo Morita 2015 Hanadeka™.

ISBN 978-1-84634-979-9

12 11 10 9 8 7 6 5 4 3 2

You can follow us on ▮ and ▮

Helen Exley®
16 Chalk Hill, Watford, Herts.
WD19 4BG, UK.
www.helenexley.com

Helen Exley®

I Love Cats

BY PAM BROWN

EDITED BY MARTIN KERR

Helen Exley®

How small a creature

to hold one's heart.

Dear cat, exasperating cat,
we love you. We turn to you
in sadness, in loneliness,
in sickness. Dear cat.
Dear comfort. Dear friend.

An ecstatic cat,
welcoming you home, can purr
so loudly it makes you
laugh out loud with joy.

Round, misty-blue eyes
stare desperately.
Love me, they say, let me into
your life – so that I can begin
to take over your entire existence.

The smallest kitten
only needs a week
to be in full possession of a house
and its owners.

How comforting

the gentle snoring of

a little cat.

C
ats give us life.
Sleeping, tuning their heartbeats
to our own,

singing away sorrow,
unravelling the day.
Sharing the empty dark.

A cat is never bored.
At a loose end he will remove all
the keys from their hooks,
climb the north face of the bookcase
or eat the rubber plant.

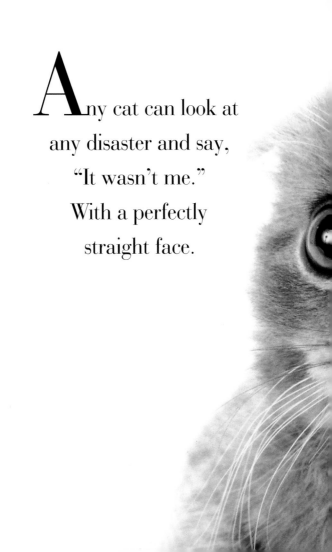

Any cat can look at
any disaster and say,
"It wasn't me."
With a perfectly
straight face.

A cat expects
to be adored.

In mid chase she stops. Sits.
Washes her feet.
Stares at you with disapproval.
"For heaven's sake woman,"
she declares.
"Act your age."

No need to watch oneself,
or act a part. One's cat knows
one is fairly stupid –
but doesn't mind.

Cat has always known
his lineage was more distinguished
than any Pharaoh.
And has lived his life accordingly.

A cat cannot speak –
but he can still give orders.

A disembowelled sofa
is as comfortable to a cat as
an intact sofa.
He can't understand why you mind
his rearranging it.

After scolding one's cat
one looks into its face and is seized
by the ugly suspicion that it
understood every word.
And has filed it for reference.

A cross kitten
comes across the room,
burning with rage – his fur
on end. At all costs do not
laugh at him.
A kitten has his pride.

It doesn't matter if you are
six feet four and broad of
shoulder, if a kitten is looking
for a mother-figure you're it.

A little cat, a little lonely cat.
Hurt. Afraid. Astounded by
kindness. Rescued. Safe.
A little life. A little hope
for humankind.

There are quiet, shy, gentle kittens, and comic, bold as brass kittens. And all beautiful. And all needing a human being who will think them the very best kitten in the universe.

Cats you must realize,
have quietly taken over the world.

Human beings
are drawn to cats because
they are all we are not –
self-contained, elegant in
everything they do, relaxed, assured.

So small so full of love
and ingenuity.
So frail so full of life.

love

All cat owners sometimes suspect that their cat knows very well what they are saying but prefers not to admit it.

They don't see why they should
waste time learning words.
After all they have no intention
of obeying anyone.

Who needs TV
when there's a kitten around?

A cat means to do everything with elegance and is horribly embarrassed if he fails.

If a cat is set on loving you
there's very little you can do about it.
He sings, he strokes, he nuzzles.
He licks and delicately
claws one's hair.

A cat allows you to sleep on the bed. On the edge.

A cat will share your bed –
just as long as you don't fidget
or breathe too heavily.

It is wise
to never wiggle one's toes in bed.
Your cat will take it as an
invitation to a vigorous game
of cat and mouse.

Cats are mysterious,
elegant, beautiful. Cats are ridiculous,
unpredictable...
and deeply disobedient.
Love as they choose to love.
Cats are who they decide to be.

A cat is the bridge that links us
to the wild wood
and the time beyond time.

He is a kindly cat, loving beyond reason; head-butter; nuzzler; flubsy sprawl of fur, belly spread, he lies like an upturned table, forepaws kneading. Demanding notice and a rub-a-tum.

Like flowers,
inexhaustible in beauty.
Like flowers, most necessary –
in ways we scarcely understand.
Healers.
Companions.
Mysteries.

One small cat
changes coming home
to an empty house
to coming home.

A cat does not need to demonstrate his affection wildly. A leaning against your legs. A chirrup. A gentle paw. "I'm glad you're home."

A cat has a wild and secretive face, and the face it shows the one it loves.

All over the world
people are sitting, or lying,
in extreme discomfort rather
than disturb the cat.

A cat can be obedient
if it suits him. It usually doesn't.

When the heart is desolate
a little cat will warm and comfort it.

The gentle touch of an
outstretched paw.
The butt of a head.
...the trust and affection
of a little cat.

We seek beauty,
poise, grace, elegance.
The cat does not.
He has them already.

To some blind souls
all cats are much alike.
To a cat lover
every cat from the
beginning of time
has been utterly
amazingly unique.

How good it is
to live with a cat – for a cat
does not look for perfection,
only food, shelter
a cuddle when it needs it,
and someone adept
at stroking.

To possess a cat
is to be a part of
a world wide company
of devoted slaves.

There is nothing so asleep
as a kitten.

A cat never ceases
to be astounded by your stupidity.
After all, he has explained
a dozen times
how to open the back door.

Cats know, quietly
and with complete conviction,
that they are
the superior species.

at says:

Now is the time for stillness.

Gentle my fur and I will sing for you.

And my song will soothe

your heart to quietness.

I don't think the word "relax" was invented until the discovery of The Cat.

A cat is of course
capable of remarkable feats
but prefers not to pursue them.

A cat could talk
if he wanted to.
But he doesn't.

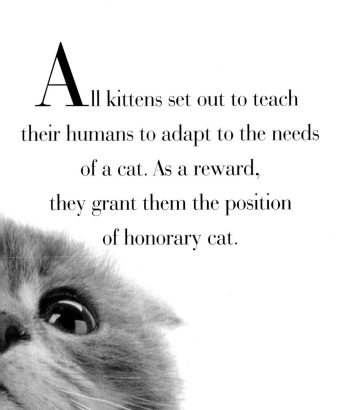

All kittens set out to teach their humans to adapt to the needs of a cat. As a reward, they grant them the position of honorary cat.

She has no words,
but by small touchings
and buttings,
she shows her love for you
and tries to distract you
from your sorrow.

How did cats come to mean
so much to humankind?
Because they cuddle close and purr
and comfort us.

...they weave themselves into
our lives and become
a part of our existence.

My cat and I are growing old together. We love sleep and food and watching the world go by.

We play together.

Doze away the summer afternoons
together. Rest in a shared
contentment.
You are part of our family –
what would we do
without you?

...his purr overflows hi

The beauties of an ordinary cat
can fill a drowsy afternoon
with wonder. No need for long
safaris – the marvel purrs
upon your lap.

heart to fill the room.

Stop scratching your cat

for one moment

and a single paw

reaches out and reminds

you to resume.

The memory that never leaves you
is of a little cat
reaching up to ask you to help it –
and to take it home.

So small a creature
can make so great a difference
to your life.

A little cat

has taught many of us to care, to love.

All treasured. All mourned,
however long or short
their existence.
Cats leave their imprint
on the years
that can never be erased.

Dear cats. Dear best of friends.

Pam Brown's writing on cats

Pam Brown's writing on Motherhood, on daughters, on friends –
and the rewarding relationships we have with those who are close
to us – has made her writing valued by people across the world.
But Pam Brown's abiding passion has been writing about cats.
And as a key staff writer on the Helen Exley® team her words
have complemented the superb pictures of Japanese photograp9er
Yoneo Morita. You have the resulting volume in your hands...
a beautiful, beautiful little book.

A note on Yoneo Morita's
outstanding photography

Japanese master photographer Yoneo Morita uses fisheye lenses,
which distort photographs, for his amazing dog and cat photographs.
This kind of lens was originally used scientifically to show maps and
astronomical views. In daily life, we use them as front door peephole
lenses and for security cameras.

By building on this technique, Yoneo captures and enhances
the beautiful, soulful eyes and other endearing features of people's
pets. Needless to say, his work began to be in huge demand,
and he was inundated by pet-lovers wanting him to catch the most
appealing photographs possible of their beloved cats and dogs.
Many years later, with a collection then running to thousands of
photos of cats, dogs - and indeed ducks and hamsters - his work
started to be used all around the world, for gifts like greeting cards,
mugs, and calendars.
And then came his gift book collections, created by Helen Exley,
where Yoneo Morita's most lovable cat and dog pictures have
been matched with quotations. These collections have gone on to sell
hundreds of thousands of copies.